101 ways to have Fun with a tennis BALL

Published in 2003 by Open Door Limited, Rutland, UK
In association with David Lloyd Leisure

Design copyright © 2003 Open Door Limited
Text copyright © 2003 Chris Dunkley

Design: Open Door Limited
Editing: Mary Morton
Printed by Imago Publishing

OPEN DOOR LIMITED

Title: 101 Ways to Have Fun with a Tennis Ball
ISBN: 1 902322 05 3

You and Your Tennis Ball

This is a fun book designed for you to learn and practise your skills with a tennis ball. It shows you lots of ways to become very skilful, to become your own champion, or to challenge your mum, dad or your friends. Each section will help you learn new skills, practise them, record your progress, become your own champion and challenge others. The equipment you need will consist mainly of objects found in the home – for example empty plastic bottles, a bucket, video boxes, a ruler, pencil, tape measure, etc. – and each activity will tell you which pieces of equipment you need. However, you will need a watch/clock with a second hand or digital dial to time some of the activities.

QUESTION: Why is David Beckham so good at free kicks?

ANSWER: Because he practises them over and over again.

Remember, you may like to try some of the activities over and over again. This is good as practise makes perfect and more practise makes champions.

*YOU CAN PLOT YOUR BEST RESULTS ON THE MASTER CHART SUPPLIED THAT ENCOURAGES YOU TO BECOME A CHAMPION IN MANY BALL SKILLS (SEE SEPARATE CHART)

What Tennis Ball Skills Do I Have?

ANSWER THESE QUESTIONS	YES OR NO
1. Can you balance the ball on your hand?	yes
2. Can you roll the ball?	yes
3. Can you bounce the ball and catch it?	no aquite
4. Can you throw the ball underarm?	
5. Can you throw the ball overarm?	
6. Can you throw the ball in the air and catch it?	

Which activity were you best at – 1, 2, 3, 4, 5 or 6 (circle your answer)?

These are the skills you need to be good at. This book will help you to take them to new heights so let's move on.

*REMEMBER – WHEN YOU RECORD YOUR BEST SCORES, PUT THEM DOWN AS THEY REALLY ARE. BE A GOOD KID – DON'T KID YOURSELF!!!

Balance the Ball

To practise these skills, keep your hand flat and your fingers together, with your palm facing upwards.

ACTIVITY	TIME SECONDS		
	10	20	30
1 Balance the ball on your right hand.			
My longest balance was:	--------	--------	--------
2 Balance the ball on your left hand.			
My longest balance was:	--------	--------	--------

Balance the Ball

ACTIVITY

3 Can you keep the ball on your hand and walk with it?

The length of your lounge:
Up the stairs:
Round the table:

4 Can you sit down on the floor and get up again without losing control of the ball?

5 How many times can you do it without losing control?

YES OR NO

RIGHT HAND	LEFT HAND
------------	------------
----------	----------
------------	----------
------------	----------

NO. OF TIMES

------------	------------

Balance the Ball

6 Can you balance the ball on your right hand whilst standing on one leg? Try the following and count to 10.

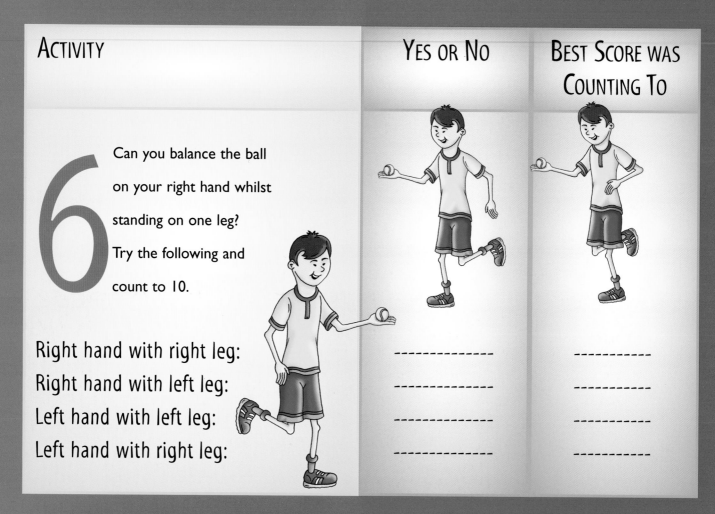

Right hand with right leg: --------------   ----------

Right hand with left leg: --------------   ----------

Left hand with left leg: --------------   ----------

Left hand with right leg: --------------   ----------

Having tried these activities I think I am...

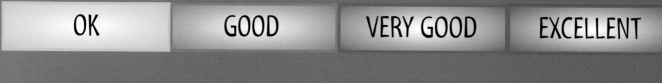

| OK | GOOD | VERY GOOD | EXCELLENT |

...at balancing a ball.

Rolling the Ball

When rolling the ball use an underarm motion and, remember, it must stay in touch with the ground – no bouncing or bobbling.

Practise rolling the ball with both hands, try to roll it slowly, try to roll it quickly across the floor – keep it under control.

Try these skills:

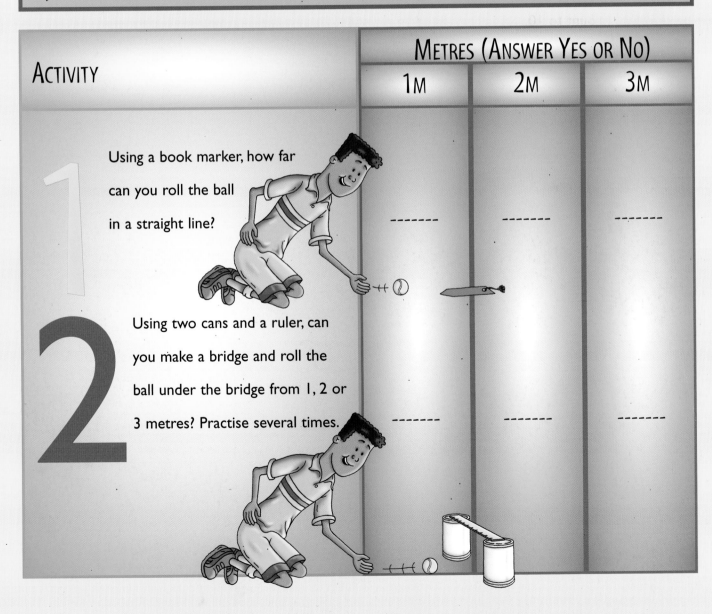

ACTIVITY

	METRES (ANSWER YES OR NO)		
	1M	2M	3M
1 Using a book marker, how far can you roll the ball in a straight line?	-------	-------	-------
2 Using two cans and a ruler, can you make a bridge and roll the ball under the bridge from 1, 2 or 3 metres? Practise several times.	-------	-------	-------

Rolling the Ball

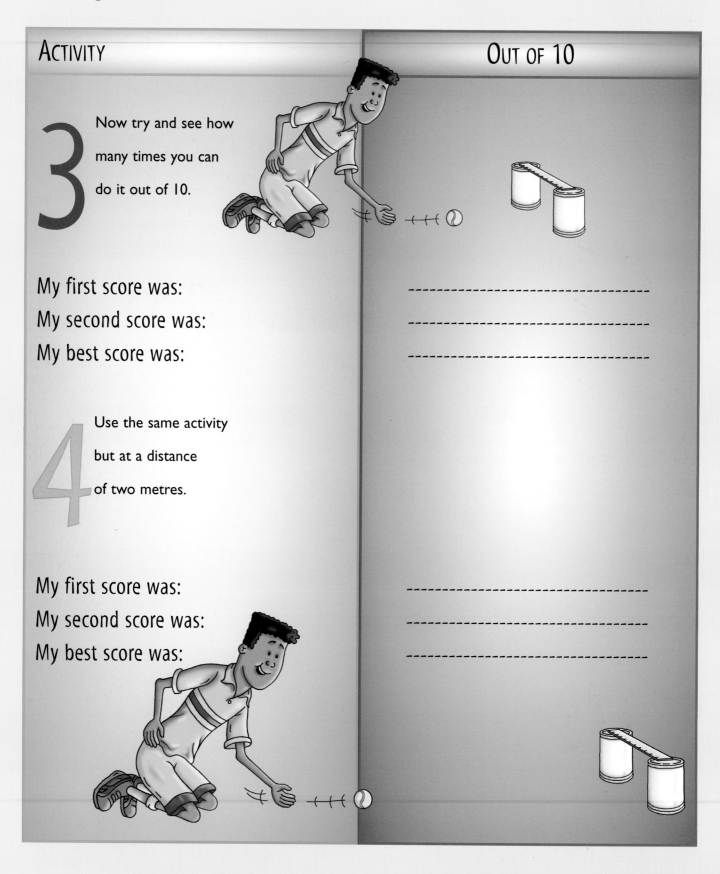

3 Now try and see how many times you can do it out of 10.

My first score was:

My second score was:

My best score was:

----

4 Use the same activity but at a distance of two metres.

My first score was:

My second score was:

My best score was:

Rolling the Ball

ACTIVITY

5 For this activity you will need six empty plastic bottles of the same size – for skittles is the name of the game! Arrange them in the shape of a triangle one in the front, two in the next row and finally three in the back row (see below). The bottles need to be one bottle length apart. Record your scores as you try to knock them over – you have five goes.

My best score with one roll was:

TRY	SCORE
First try:	------------------
Second try:	------------------
Third try:	------------------
Fourth try:	------------------
Fifth try:	------------------

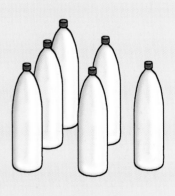

Rolling the Ball

This is a good game to play with your mum and dad or your friends.

NO. OF SHOTS

6 Using the same bottles, put them around the room (two big steps apart) and make a mini golf course. From a starting point see how many rolls it takes to knock them all over one at a time. Record your score.

On my first round I took:

On my second round I took:

Having practised, my best score so far is:

My friend's best score was:

My mum's/dad's best score was:

See if you can make up a rolling game of your own.

Bouncing and Catching

Practise bouncing and catching the ball using two hands or one hand. Take the ball for a walk, bouncing and catching as you go. Try moving in and out of objects but keep control of the ball. Now see if you can do these activities:

ACTIVITY	SUCCESSFUL CATCHES

1 Bounce with one hand and catch with two.

In 20 seconds I did: ------------------------------------

In 30 seconds I did: ------------------------------------

In one minute I did: ------------------------------------

2 Bounce with your right hand and catch with your right hand.

In 20 seconds I did: ------------------------------------

In 30 seconds I did: ------------------------------------

In one minute I did: ------------------------------------

3 Bounce with your right hand and catch with your left hand.

In 20 seconds I did: ------------------------------------

In 30 seconds I did: ------------------------------------

In one minute I did: ------------------------------------

Bouncing and Catching

4 Bounce with your left hand and catch with your left hand.

In 20 seconds I did:

In 30 seconds I did:

In one minute I did:

_____

_____

_____

5 Bounce with your left hand and catch with your right hand.

In 20 seconds I did:

In 30 seconds I did:

In one minute I did:

_____

_____

_____

Bouncing and Catching

6 Bouncing and catching at different heights. Practise bouncing and catching the ball at knee, waist, chest and head height. Now see if you can do all four in a row.

Knee ----------------------------

Waist ----------------------------

Chest ----------------------------

Head ----------------------------

All four ----------------------------

If you are good at this, see if you can do one after another.

IN A ROW

7 Record your best score (eg "my best score was three in a row").

My best score was:

I beat my best score by doing:

Bouncing and Catching

ACTIVITY

8 Zig-zag bouncing and catching. Using the six bottles you had for your game of skittles, arrange them in a straight line one metre apart. Now practise moving in and out and up the line. Go round the last bottle and come back the same way. If you feel good at this, time yourself to zig-zag there and back (if you knock any skittles over, it does not count!)

SECONDS

My first attempt took: ----------------------------------

My second attempt took: ----------------------------------

My third attempt took: ----------------------------------

My quickest time was: ----------------------------------

Can you beat this time (YES/NO)? ----------------------------------

My new record time is: ----------------------------------

Try some of these games with your friends or make up some bouncing and catching games of your own.

Throwing Underarm

To practise the underarm throw, hold the ball in your hand with your palm facing upwards, stretch your arm out straight in front of you, take your arm down at your side and then bring it up, releasing the ball in the direction you want it to go.

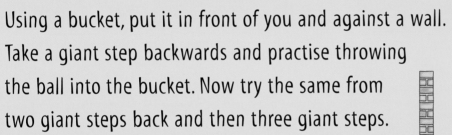

Using a bucket, put it in front of you and against a wall. Take a giant step backwards and practise throwing the ball into the bucket. Now try the same from two giant steps back and then three giant steps.

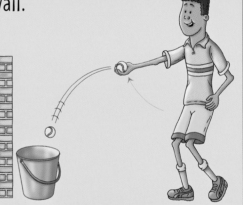

Choosing a mark of one step back, see how many times you can get the ball in the bucket out of 10 tries. Now try the same for two and three steps back.

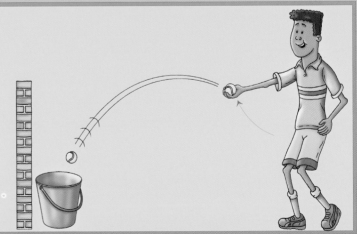

Throwing Underarm

ACTIVITY			NO. OF TRIES		
		1ST	2ND	3RD	BEST SCORE
1 step back		-------	-------	-------	-------
2 steps back		-------	-------	-------	-------
3 steps back		-------	-------	-------	-------

Try this game against your mum, dad or a friend. You can put their score next to yours on a separate sheet.

To make the game more difficult set it up in the same way. You start at three steps back but you put a chair halfway between you and the bucket. Now can you throw the ball underarm over the chair and into the bucket? This is difficult so practise before you record your scores.

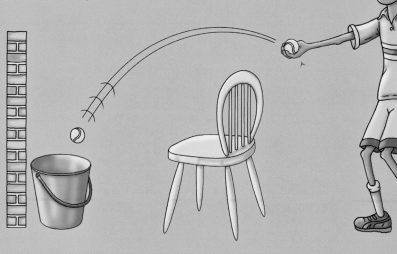

With all the games try over and over again until you are really good. Just remember – practise makes perfect!

Throwing Overarm

In its simplest form the overarm throw is like throwing a dart at a dart board. At its most difficult it's like throwing a ball from the boundary in cricket or a baseball from the deep. For your practise we will use the simple way indoors and try the full throw when outside.

ACTIVITY

1 Practise the game you played with the bucket in the last section but this time start three steps away, then try four steps and finally, five steps.

Record your best score out of 10.

BEST SCORE (OUT OF 10)

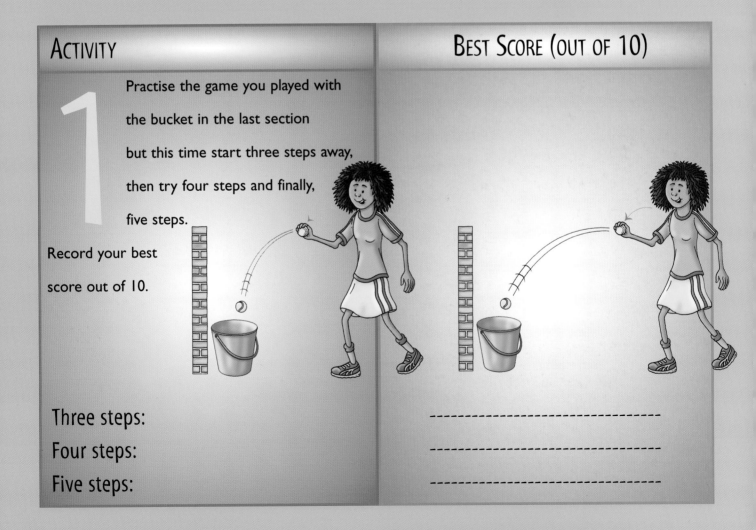

Three steps: _____

Four steps: _____

Five steps: _____

Throwing Overarm

ACTIVITY

2 Target Time – you will need five empty video boxes or five empty plastic bottles. Line them up in a row of five, and put a ruler three steps away from the line of targets; this is where you throw from. Have some practise throws before you start. Now record how many throws it takes to knock them all over.

My first go took:

My second go took:

My third go took:

Try to beat your best score:

My new record score of:

Ask your mum or dad or your friend to try and beat your score

My best score was:

THROWS TO KNOCK THEM ALL OVER

Throwing Overarm

ACTIVITY

3

Boxing Clever – you will need three boxes: one small, one medium and one large and three tennis balls.

Set the boxes up three steps away.

Using the large box first, see how long it takes to throw the three balls in. Then try the medium box and, finally, the small box. Now put the boxes next to each other and see if you can get the first ball in the large box, the second in the medium, the third in the small. Time yourself to complete the skill.

Large, medium and small,
one ball in each took:

Large, medium and small,
two balls in each took:

Large, medium and small,
three balls in each took:

SECONDS

Throwing Overarm

ACTIVITY	SECONDS
Test yourself – see if you can do three in a row large to medium to small:	----------------------------------
How long did it take (record the time)?	----------------------------------
In beating this time I took:	----------------------------------
My record time was:	----------------------------------
See if your mum, dad or a friend can beat your time?	----------------------------------

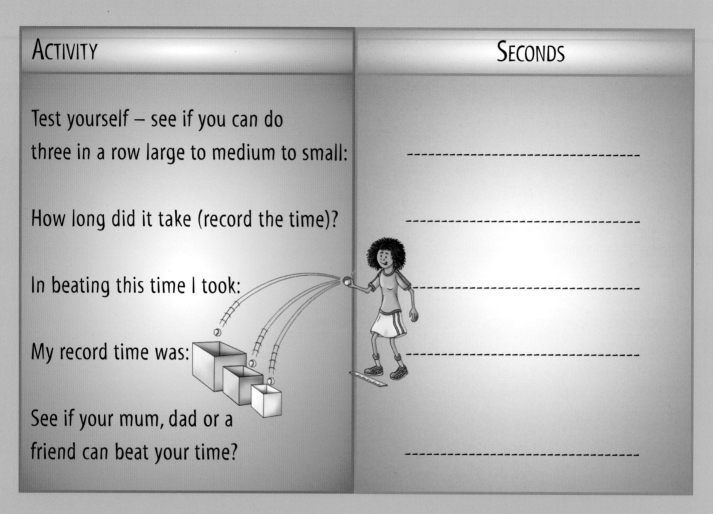

Having tried these activities, I think I am:

| OK | GOOD | VERY GOOD | EXCELLENT |

At throwing the ball overarm I rate myself as:

| OK | GOOD | VERY GOOD | EXCELLENT |

Catching the Ball in the Air

This is an important skill and one you need to be very good at, so try to become a champion catcher in all that you do.

ACTIVITY

1 Freeplay –

practise catching the ball;

Throw it up with two hands and catch with two.

Throw it up with one hand and catch with two.

Throw it up with one hand and catch with one.

You can have fun with this indoors, but try and keep the ball under control at all times.

Catching the Ball in the Air

Fun and Games

2

NO. OF TRIES (OUT OF 10)

Throw with two hands, catch with two —

1st: ------------------------------

2nd: ------------------------------

3rd" ------------------------------

Best score: ------------------------------

Throw with one hand, catch with two —

1st: ------------------------------

2nd: ------------------------------

3rd: ------------------------------

Best score: ------------------------------

Throw with one hand, catch with one —

1st: ------------------------------

2nd: ------------------------------

3rd: ------------------------------

Best score: ------------------------------

Catching the Ball in the Air

3 Throw, Clap and Catch –
throw the ball in the air, clap your
hands once and catch the ball.
Do the same again but clap twice.
Now clap three times, then keep
going up to five.

I can throw, clap and catch...

once:

twice:

three times:

four times:

five times:

more than five:

ANSWER YES, NO, OR NOT YET

Catching the Ball in the Air

ACTIVITY

4 Turn and Catch – this is difficult so practise this.
Throw the ball in the air and turn round completely, catching the ball at the end of your turn.

PUT A TICK WHEN YOU CAN DO IT

Once: ------------------

Twice: ------------------

Three times: ------------------

My record score is: ------------------------------------

Tennis Ball Skills

CHAMP

Name: ....

Top 10 Activities	OK	GOOD	VERY C

How to Use Your Chart

Write the names of your 10 favourite activities. As you improve on these colour in the box underneath the rating
Now colour your new rating on the chart. Keep trying and improving until all your columns are coloured in and y

Congratulations Champ! You have done really well! Don't st

ION CHART

OOD	EXCELLENT	CHAMPION	GOLD MEDAL
			✦
			✦
			✦
			✦
			✦
			✦
			✦
			✦
			✦
			✦

. If you need to improve on any of them, go back to the book and practise some more!
u reach **CHAMPION**! - Then give yourself a **GOLD MEDAL**!

David Lloyd

p - keep developing your skills to become a **SUPER CHAMP!**

Catching the Ball in the Air

ACTIVITY

5 Throw, Head and Catch –
practise throwing the ball in the air,
heading it like a footballer
and then catching it.

In 30 seconds I did:

In one minute I did:

RECORD YOUR BEST SCORES

CATCHES	BEST SCORES
--------------	-----------
--------------	-----------

Having tried these activities, I think I am:

OK   GOOD   VERY GOOD   EXCELLENT

at catching the ball in the air.

Putting Your Skills Together

See if you can put your new skills together and combine them so you become more and more expert.

ACTIVITY	ANSWER (YES, NO OR NOT YET)

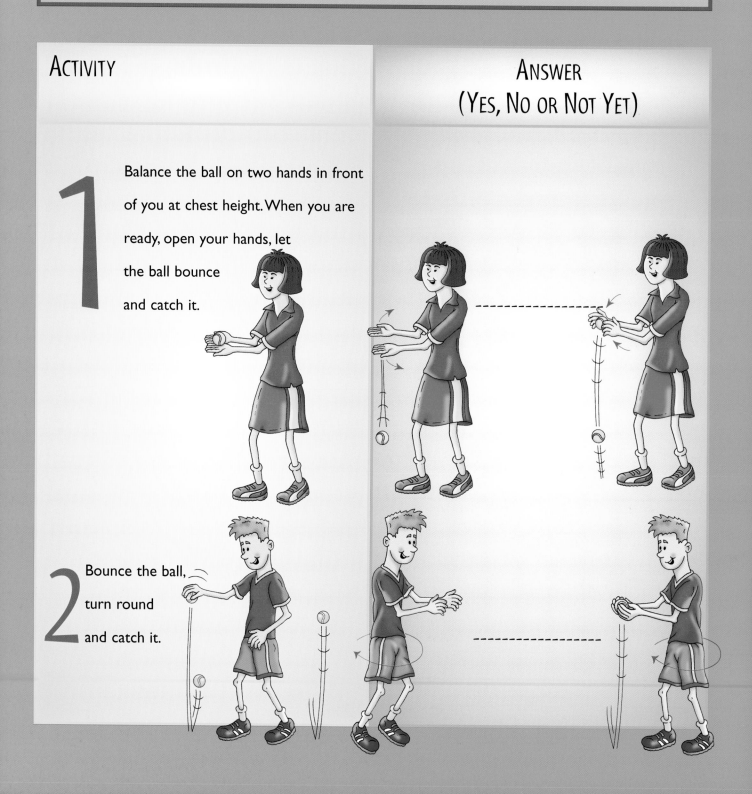

1 Balance the ball on two hands in front of you at chest height. When you are ready, open your hands, let the ball bounce and catch it.

2 Bounce the ball, turn round and catch it.

Putting Your Skills Together

ACTIVITY	ANSWER (YES, NO OR NOT YET)

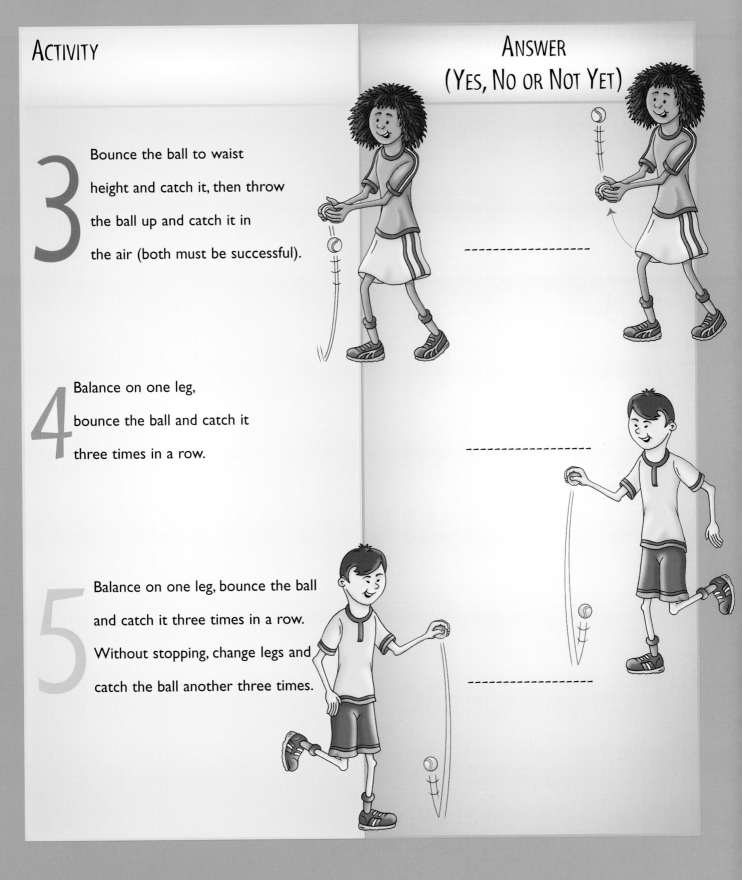

3 Bounce the ball to waist height and catch it, then throw the ball up and catch it in the air (both must be successful).

----

4 Balance on one leg, bounce the ball and catch it three times in a row.

----

5 Balance on one leg, bounce the ball and catch it three times in a row. Without stopping, change legs and catch the ball another three times.

Putting Your Skills Together

ACTIVITY	ANSWER (YES, NO OR NOT YET)

6 Roll the ball along the floor, then run and pick it up. Gently toss it over your head, turn round and catch it after one bounce.

----

7 Do the same as above but try to catch the ball before it bounces.

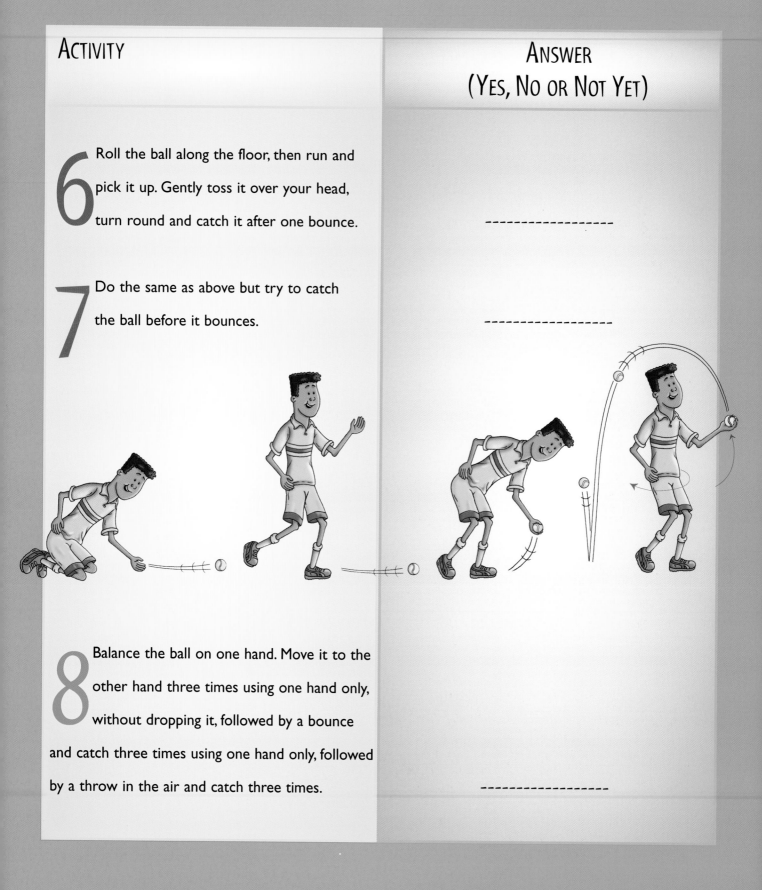

8 Balance the ball on one hand. Move it to the other hand three times using one hand only, without dropping it, followed by a bounce and catch three times using one hand only, followed by a throw in the air and catch three times.

Putting Your Skills Together

ACTIVITY

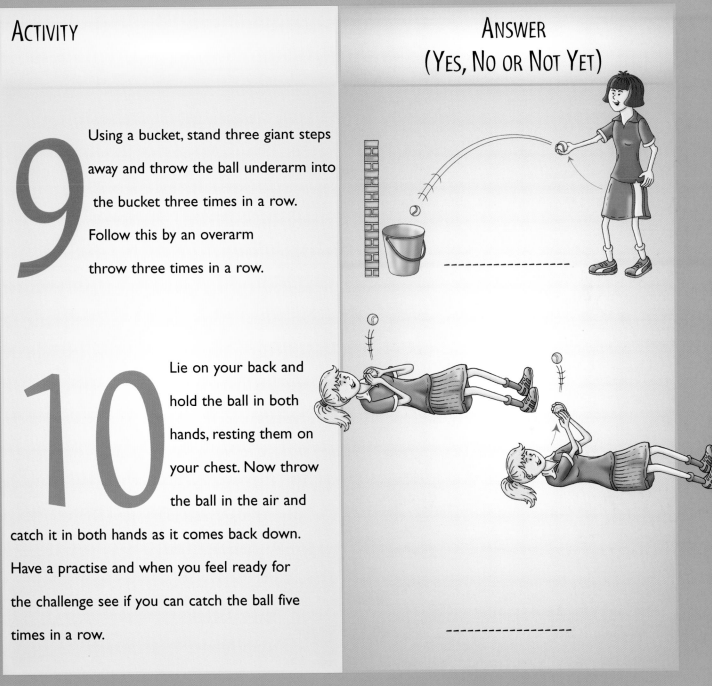

9 Using a bucket, stand three giant steps away and throw the ball underarm into the bucket three times in a row. Follow this by an overarm throw three times in a row.

----

10 Lie on your back and hold the ball in both hands, resting them on your chest. Now throw the ball in the air and catch it in both hands as it comes back down. Have a practise and when you feel ready for the challenge see if you can catch the ball five times in a row.

After trying these TOP 10 how do you rate yourself?

| OK | GOOD | VERY GOOD | EXCELLENT | CHAMPION |

A Circuit of Ball Skills

The idea is to complete all of the activities successfully in order from 1 to 10 and to time yourself.

You start the clock at the beginning (Skill 1) and stop it immediately after the last exercise (Skill 10).

You may have a practise round before you start.

Set up the circuit using the following activities, making sure that you can move from 1 to 2 to 3 to 4 and so on up to 10 (try to get your mum or dad to help you set up the circuit).

A Circuit of Ball Skills

CIRCUIT SKILLS

1 Balance the ball on one hand and walk the length of your lounge (if you drop the ball, go back and start again). Move on to...

2 Roll the ball the length of your lounge (try to keep it in a straight line). Move on to...

3 Bounce the ball with one hand and catch with two. Do this five times in a row then move on to...

A Circuit of Ball Skills

CIRCUIT SKILLS

4 Bounce the ball with one hand and catch it with one hand 3 times in a row. Move on to...

5 Underarm bucket throw – with the bucket against the wall put a marker two giant steps away from it. Now see if you can throw the ball into the bucket three times in a row. When successful move on to...

6 Overarm bucket throw – use the same set up as for Skill 5 and throw the ball into the bucket three times in a row. Move on to...

7 Throw the ball, clap once, catch, throw, clap twice, catch and throw, clap three times, and catch. Complete all three in a row then move on to...

A Circuit of Ball Skills

CIRCUIT SKILLS

8 Balance on one leg, throw the ball in the air and catch it five times in a row. Move on to...

9 Bounce the ball, catch it, throw it in the air and catch it. Do this combined activity three times in a row and finally move on to...

10 Lie on your back, throw the ball in the air and catch it three times in a row.

A Circuit of Ball Skills

Now record your time for the completed circuit.

ACTIVITY	MINUTES, SECONDS
My first circuit took:	------------------
My second circuit took:	------------------
My third circuit took:	------------------
My best time is:	------------------
Ask your mum, dad or a friend to have a go and record their time.	------------------

I found the circuit:

When it becomes easy, you are doing really well.

Playing in the Garden

Developing your tennis ball skills outside gives you more space to improve your skills even further. These activities and games will help you to move towards being a champion.

ACTIVITY

BEST SCORE OUT OF 10

1 Find a wall (not near a window!!!!) and see if you can practise these skills Always start two giant steps back from the wall. KEEP YOUR SCORE OUT OF 10.

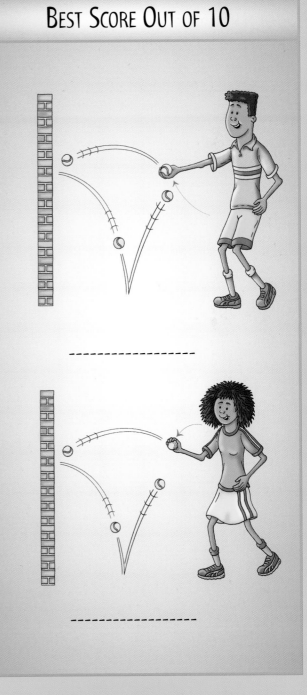

Underarm throw against the wall, letting the ball bounce and catching it. My best score was:

Overarm throw against the wall, letting the ball bounce and catching it. My best score was:

Playing in the Garden

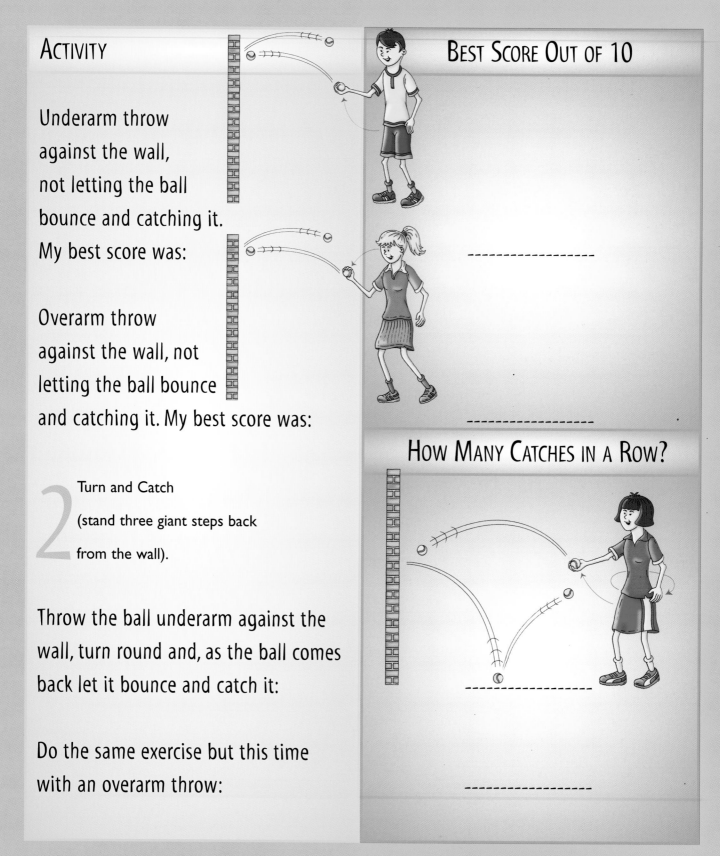

ACTIVITY

Underarm throw against the wall, not letting the ball bounce and catching it. My best score was:

Overarm throw against the wall, not letting the ball bounce and catching it. My best score was:

2 Turn and Catch (stand three giant steps back from the wall).

Throw the ball underarm against the wall, turn round and, as the ball comes back let it bounce and catch it:

Do the same exercise but this time with an overarm throw:

BEST SCORE OUT OF 10

HOW MANY CATCHES IN A ROW?

Playing in the Garden

3

Target Time (ask your mum or dad to help your put a circular target on the wall about the size of a car wheel – draw it on with chalk or cut out a piece of card and stick it on). Standing three giant steps away, how many times out of five can you get it inside the target using:

underarm right hand?   ------------------

underarm left hand?   ------------------

overarm right hand?   ------------------

overarm left hand?   ------------------

I was best at: ------------------

I was worst at: ------------------

* TRY TO MAKE YOUR WORST AS GOOD AS YOUR BEST.

Playing in the Garden

4 Three in a Row. Roll the ball so it hits the wall and returns to you, then underarm throw into the target. Let it bounce and catch it. Finally throw the ball overarm into the target let it bounce and catch it.

How many can you do in one minute?

My best score in one minute is:

----

5 Can you invent some games of your own using your ball skills? Try them out with your friends.

At the Park

Here are some ideas for you to try in the park but, remember, keep your tennis ball under control, do not disturb other people with it, and look out for dogs – they might borrow your ball and not bring it back!!!!!

Also you may want to record your efforts – you may not. Either way, the park is a useful place in which to practise your skills.

ACTIVITY	YES OR NO

1 Swings, roundabouts, slides and see-saws.

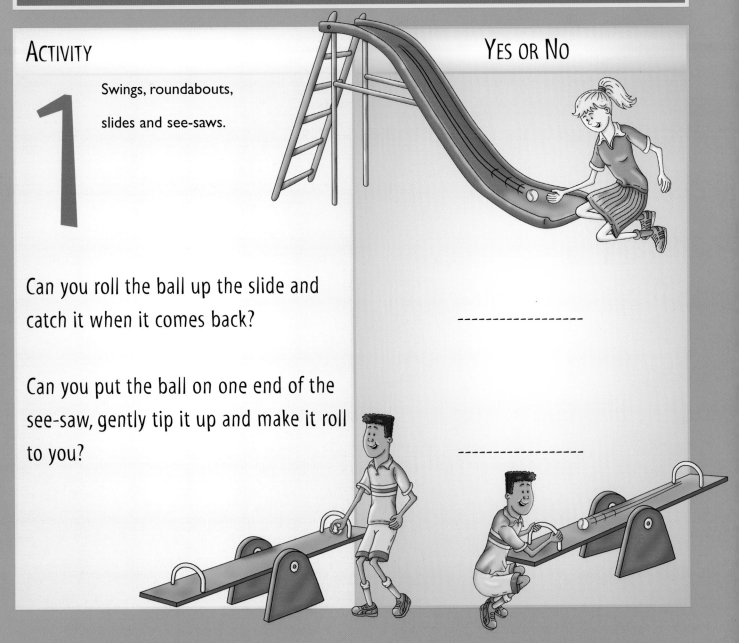

Can you roll the ball up the slide and catch it when it comes back?

Can you put the ball on one end of the see-saw, gently tip it up and make it roll to you?

At the Park

Swing a toddler swing gently and when it comes towards you, can you get the ball to land and stay on the swing? Do this activity very slowly as it is difficult.

Put a target on the roundabout and set it turning gently. Can you hit it with your ball as it goes by?

Sit on the roundabout and as you go round get your mum or dad to toss the ball to you. Can you catch it?

At the Park

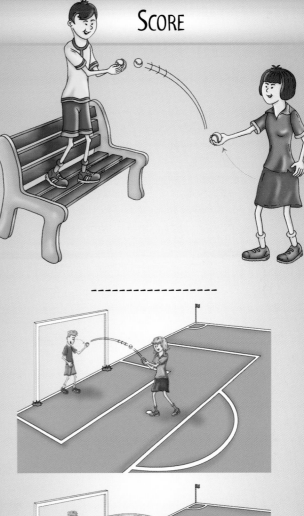

2 Balance and Catch.
Stand on a park bench or a cut-down tree stump and throw and catch the ball to yourself or get your mum or dad to throw the ball to you.

How many can you catch in a row?

----

3 How far can you throw? Using a football pitch, stand in the goal and get your mum or dad to stand in various places and see if you can throw the ball to them. For example, they could stand on the penalty spot, then the corners of the penalty area, even the centre spot if you can throw that far.

4 Stand on a line, throw the ball overarm and let it come to rest.

Count how many giant steps it went:

How many steps was your best throw?

At the Park

ACTIVITY

5 Basketball/Netball Targets. Some parks have areas with basketball or netball rings. If you have one where you live, try and spend some time using both underarm and overarm throwing to practise getting the ball through the hoop. Scores out of 10 would be a good test. Record your best score, then try and beat it.

Score out of 10: _____

Best score: _____

At the Park

Other activities could include:

1 Football dribbling or kicking the ball against a friend.

2 Take a tennis racket.
Bounce the ball on the strings or hit the ball up in the air and catch it. Get your mum or dad to hit it up in the air for you to catch, or even go to the tennis courts and play games over the net

3 Take a hockey stick or makeshift golf club and try hitting, putting or dribbling the ball. For example, stand on the goal-line of a football pitch and see if you can play the ball and make it stop on the penalty spot.

The park is there for you to play in. Use it as a place to develop your skill with a tennis ball.

At the Seaside

ACTIVITY	ANSWER

1 Make a row of 10 sandcastles about one step apart and in a straight line. See if you can dribble the tennis ball in and out of the line and back again.

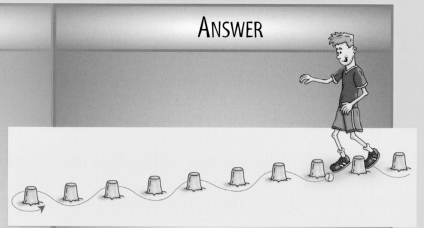

How long did it take?

Can you do it with the other foot?

----

2 Make a line in the sand and put your bucket about one metre away, lying on its side. Roll the ball into it. When you are successful, put the bucket about two metres away and so on until it is five metres away.

How many shots did you take to get to five metres?

At the Seaside

3 Draw a circle in the sand about three metres across. Around the circle dig out five or more bucket-size holes and number them. You stand in the middle and roll the ball into the holes one by one.

How many shots did you take to get round the circle?

----

4 Do the same as above but try to kick the ball into each hole.

How many shots did you take?

At the Seaside

5 Build a row of five sandcastles by a windbreak. Using an overarm throw, see how long it takes you to knock them down.

How long did it take you to knock them down

Challenge your mum, dad, brother or sister and record their times.

----

6 If you have a deck chair, lay it flat and draw a line two steps, then three steps, then four steps, then five steps away from it. Stand on the nearest line with your back to the chair and see if you can throw the ball over your head and make it land on the chair and stay there. If you can, then move to the next line and so on to the finish. See if you can find someone to challenge.

Remember the beach is similar to the park in terms of space so some of the ball activities you practise in the park can be tried on the beach, too. Have fun and try to find games of your own that will test your skill and help make you a champion.

Games You Can Play

If you have worked through this book and done well, you can now try out your skills in games and sports that will give you further fun and satisfaction. This list has only a few of the many ball games you can play – you may not know some of them or you may know of others. The more ball games you can play the better as this helps you to become really expert.

As you read down the list, tick the games you know and those you can play. You can also add your own if you wish.

Games You Can Play

ACTIVITY	I KNOW	I CAN PLAY
Five-a-side Football	------------	------------
Hockey	------------	------------
Golf	------------	------------
Rounders	------------	------------
Hopscotch	------------	------------
Tennis	------------	------------
Basketball	------------	------------
Netball	------------	------------
Badminton	------------	------------
Baseball	------------	------------
Softball	------------	------------
Mini Rugby	------------	------------
Volleyball	------------	------------
Darts	------------	------------
Cricket	------------	------------
Boules	------------	------------
----------------------	------------	------------
----------------------	------------	------------
----------------------	------------	------------
----------------------	------------	------------
----------------------	------------	------------